About the Book

Who is the baby girl in the photograph? Who is that boy
swinging on the tire? Could they be Mother and Father, a
long time ago? Like all albums, this book is full of snapshots.
Some of them are recent. Some of them were taken many
years ago. One shows a young man graduating from college.
Another shows a lovely bride.

Where I Begin shares the warmth and the surprises of one
little girl's discoveries as she turns the pages of her album.
Looking at these old (and not so old) photographs of the
family, she begins thinking about birth and death, about hap-
piness and sorrow. She may even begin wondering about the
mysterious river of time, on which all of us are moving. . . .

Rocco Negri's rich and sensitive drawings and Sarah
Abbott's poetic text make *Where I Begin* a book young
children will enjoy reading again and again.

WHERE I BEGIN

by Sarah Abbott
pictures by Rocco Negri

Coward-McCann, Inc.   New York

WHERE I BEGIN

This baby boy
laughing,
lying in the grass,
is my father
long ago.

This baby girl
staring out from all those ruffles,
with eyes like dark olives,
is my mother
long ago.

This little boy
swinging on the tire
hung from a tree
is my father
long ago.

This little girl
solemn and shy,
holding on to a lady's finger,
is my mother
long ago.

This curly-haired boy
with his hand in the collie's fur
is my father
long ago.

This pale little girl
with the doll
drooping from her hand
is my mother
long ago.

This boy
with the missing tooth,
grinning at his little sister,
is my father
long ago.

This thin little girl
curled up on the window seat,
reading,
is my mother
long ago.

This tall boy
playing guitar,
singing some song
I never heard,
is my father
long ago.

This girl
with long black hair,
the one standing in the third row,
almost smiling,
is my mother
long ago.

This young man
in the long robe
and square hat
is my father
long ago.

That girl
looking out to sea
over the railing of the ocean liner
is my mother
long ago.

That young man
standing on the sailboat
is my father
long ago.

This beautiful girl
laughing
with all those boys
is my mother
before she met my father.

This young man
leaning against a bike
under the chestnut tree
one summer in Paris
is my father
before he met my mother.

This slender girl
with her hair blowing in the wind
is my mother
the summer she and my father met.

This bride
like a white flower
is my mother . . .

the day she and my father
were married
long ago.

This young woman,
her hair piled on top of her head
and my father's arm around her,
is my mother
another summer
long ago.

This is my grandmother and grandfather,
my mother's mother and father,
when they were very old.

This big cherry tree
was planted
by my father's mother.
It shades the graves
of my father's
mother and father
and their little boy,
who died
before my father
was born.

This quiet lady,
lovely and large,
leaning against my father,
is my mother.

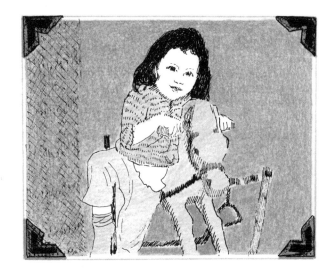

And here's where
I
begin.

About the Author

Sarah Abbott has a farm in Vermont where she spends much of her time writing. *Where I Begin* is her first book for young people.

About the Artist

Rocco Negri has illustrated a number of books for young people. He has studied at the Art Students League of New York and at the School of Visual Art. Mr. Negri lives in Ridgewood, New York with his wife and two children.